This annual belongs to:

nja

Hello!

This special book is the very first Numberjacks annual. Inside, there are lots of stories about the Numberjacks' exciting adventures. There are puzzles and problems for you to solve, too.

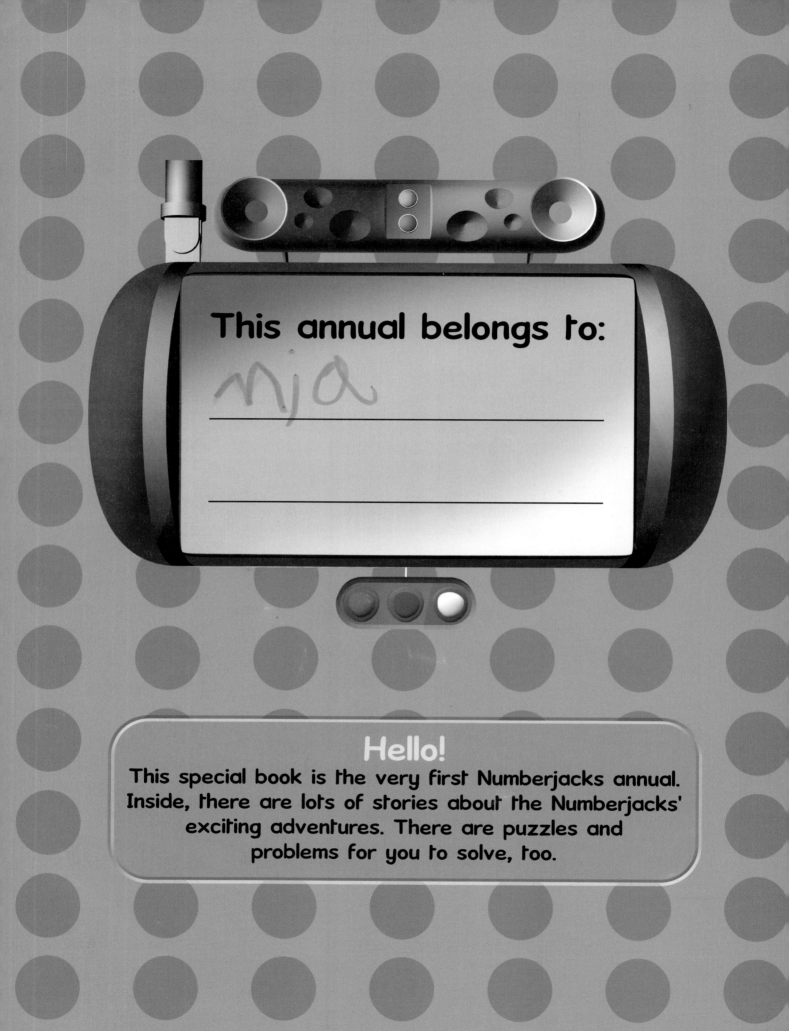

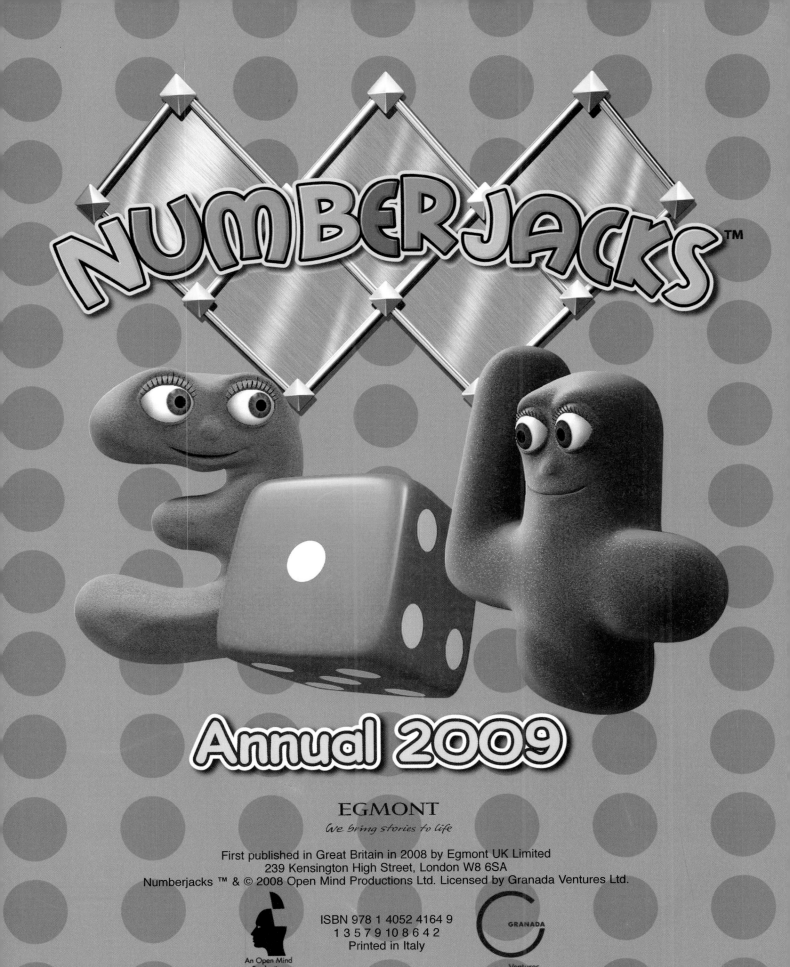

NUMBERJACKS™

Annual 2009

EGMONT
We bring stories to life

First published in Great Britain in 2008 by Egmont UK Limited
239 Kensington High Street, London W8 6SA
Numberjacks ™ & © 2008 Open Mind Productions Ltd. Licensed by Granada Ventures Ltd.

An Open Mind Production

ISBN 978 1 4052 4164 9
1 3 5 7 9 10 8 6 4 2
Printed in Italy

GRANADA
Ventures

Contents

Sing Along!

In an ordinary sofa
In an ordinary room
Are extraordinary heroes
Who are standing by to zoom
To wherever they are needed
They are speeding out today,
The Numberjacks are on their way.
They will help you with your problems,
They are waiting for your call.
No problem is too big for them,
No problem is too small.
Things may all be going wrong
But you can bet it's not for long –
The Numberjacks are on their way,
The Numberjacks are on their way!

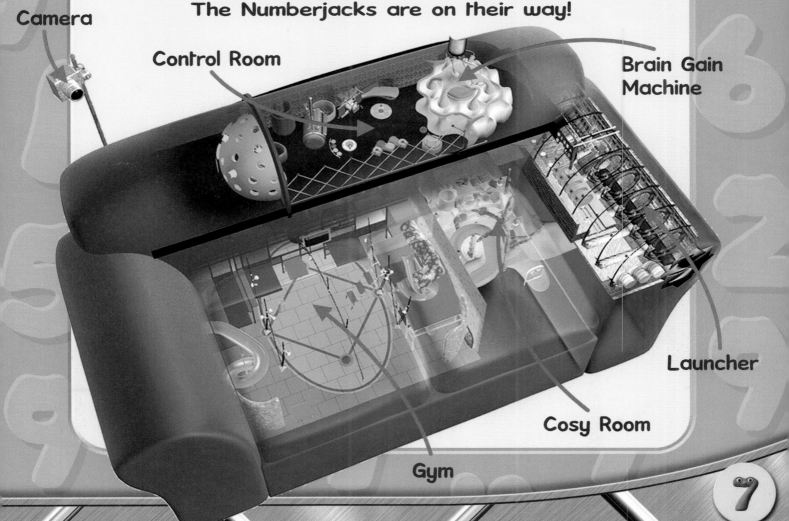

Camera

Control Room

Brain Gain Machine

Launcher

Cosy Room

Gym

Meet the Numberjacks

Who is your favourite Numberjack?

O is the baby of the Numberjacks and very special because O can make things disappear!

1 is only a little number but serious problems can happen when O comes along and makes 1 into a 1O!

2 would love to be like the bigger numbers! 2 sometimes causes trouble by making numbers go wrong.

3 loves being in the Brain Gain Machine, going out on missions, and playing with the Beautiful Things.

4 likes to be in the Control Room. 4 also likes trains and keeping things tidy.

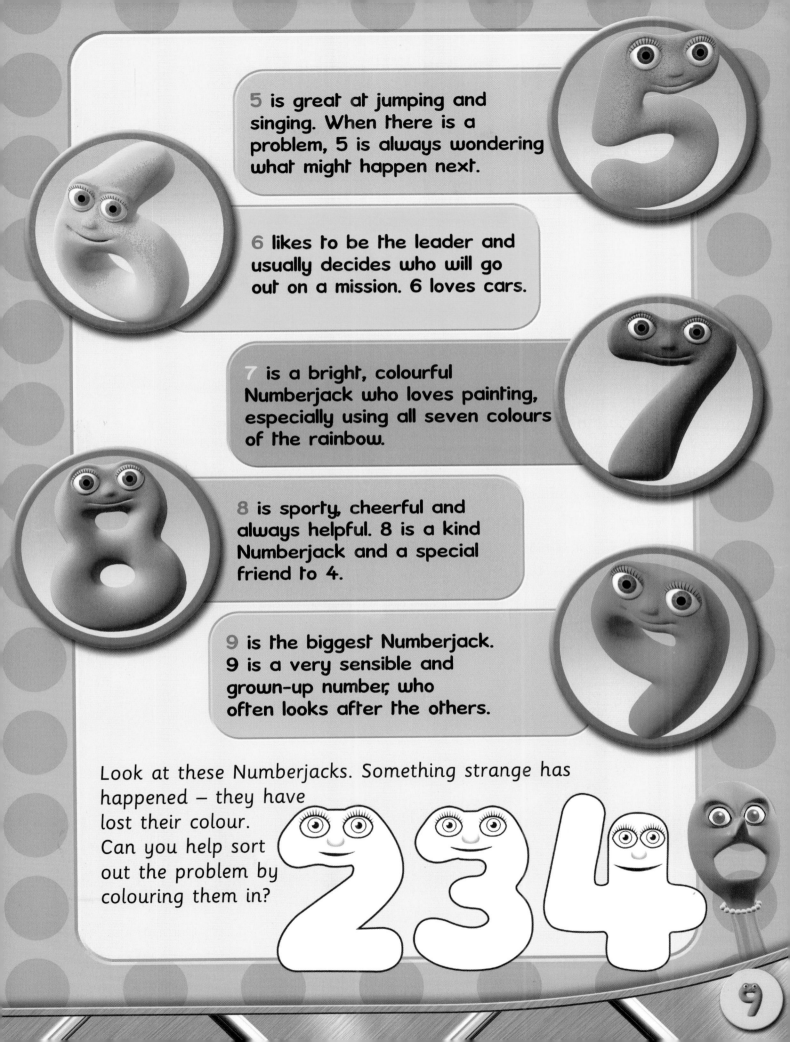

5 is great at jumping and singing. When there is a problem, 5 is always wondering what might happen next.

6 likes to be the leader and usually decides who will go out on a mission. 6 loves cars.

7 is a bright, colourful Numberjack who loves painting, especially using all seven colours of the rainbow.

8 is sporty, cheerful and always helpful. 8 is a kind Numberjack and a special friend to 4.

9 is the biggest Numberjack. 9 is a very sensible and grown-up number, who often looks after the others.

Look at these Numberjacks. Something strange has happened — they have lost their colour. Can you help sort out the problem by colouring them in?

The Control Room

This is the **Control Room**. When the Numberjacks get a call from an Agent the alarm rings and flashes.

Everyone rushes to the Control Room and the Agent tells the Numberjacks about a problem in the outside world.

The Numberjacks can see on a small screen what's happening outside.

Then one of the Numberjacks goes out on a mission to find out what can be done.

6 is outside on a mission. Where do you think 6 might be?

The Numberjack who is chosen for a mission has to be scanned, before going into the **Launcher**.

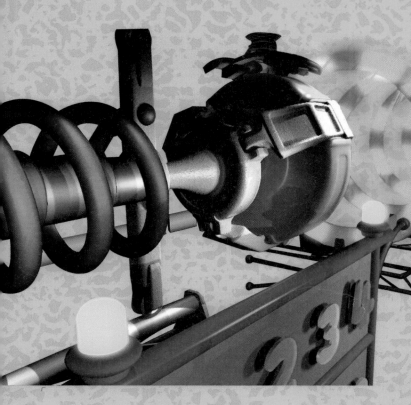

This is the Launcher. All the Numberjacks have their own special launch pod.

A camera checks the room to make sure nobody is around.

Then the Numberjacks are split into hundreds of tiny pieces as they fly out of the sofa. They quickly need to find a matching number to land on.

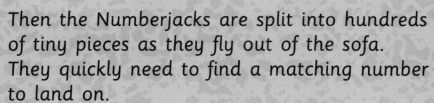

Which number could 6 land on?

 3    6    35

Brain Gain is made inside the **Brain Gain Machine**. Brain Gain is made up of all the joined-up thinking of the Numberjacks, the Agents and you! The thinking gets more and more powerful until the Brain Gain is ready to be sent to the Numberjacks on the mission.

Thinking is very strong and is how the Numberjacks sort out problems.

Sing the words to the Brain Gain song:

5 has just been sent some Brain Gain.

Brain Gain, Brain Gain,
To sort the problem use our brains,
The way to get your brains all linking up together,
Joined-up thinking.
Getting brain power now - Brain Gain!

Calling All Agents!

The Agents are very important. They are always on the lookout for problems happening in the world around them and will call the Numberjacks as soon as they see something strange. Later, they help the Numberjacks by sending in their thoughts for the Brain Gain Machine to read.

The Agents appear on the Diamond Screen. They each have their own number.

Would you like to be an Agent? Draw your face in the empty diamond. You could even get a grown-up to cut out a photo of you and stick it in place.

What do you think the problem is here?

Here's Agent 21.

13

Meet the Meanies

The **Meanies** do their best to cause problems for everyone. It can take a lot of Brain Gain to sort them out!

The **Shape Japer** can change the shape of things. She can change her own shape, too.

What shape is her face now?

The **Puzzler** sometimes makes giant bubbles to trap the Numberjacks inside.

Solve this puzzle to free 7.

How many bubbles can you see?
Do you think you can beat me?
If you're right, then 7 goes free!

Answer: Her face is a square (her body is a cube).

Answer: 7 bubbles.

Spooky Spoon loves to stir things up for the Numberjacks. She's swapped the bowling balls for these other balls!

The **Numbertaker** is a trouble-maker who loves to take different numbers or groups of things.

How many tomatoes is the Numbertaker taking?

If you spot a tell-tale glob of slime then the **Problem Blob** is making trouble! Look out, 4!

What colour is the Problem Blob's slime?

Answers: 4 tomatoes; green slime.

15

Going Wrong

5 was singing a number rap: "I say one, two, three, four, five. We're the numbers and we're alive."

"I bet I could sing for longer than you," said 3. "Starting now – La, la, la, la, la, la, la, la, la, la . . ."

"Argh, argh, I'm going mad!" said 4, jumping upside down into a box to escape 3's singing.

Poor old 4! Can you see anything else on this page that is upside down?

Suddenly, the alarm sounded – a call was coming in! The Numberjacks hurried straight to the Control Room.

"I think I've spotted a problem. There's a boy having trouble with his pencil," said Agent 16, on the Diamond Screen.

The Numberjacks could see a boy with a pencil that was **growing**!

"We'll be right there!" 6 told the Agent.

6 asked 4 to go on the mission.

"OK," said 4, nervously. 4 was worried about the launch.

"All clear," said 3, after checking the screen.

4 flew out from the sofa into the outside world. 3 had to quickly find a number four for 4 to land on. Just in time, Agent 16 asked the boy to write a four with his very long pencil so that 4 could land safely on it.

What has happened to the boy's pencil?

Who checked the launch screen?

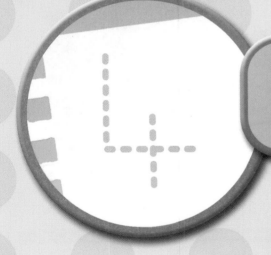

Draw a four here so that Numberjack 4 can land on it!

At first, 4 couldn't work out why the pencil was growing. Agent 53 told 4 to look really closely.

Look closely. Can you see anything on the pencil?

17

"Look – slime!" said 6.

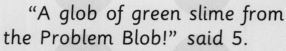

A glob of green slime from the Problem Blob!" said 5.

The Numberjacks didn't know how to sort out the Problem Blob but then the Agents rang in to help.

"That pencil's too long," said Agent 28. "You've got to make it **shorter**."

"Get the Brain Gain Machine going," said 6.

"I can do it! Just watch me! Shorter, shorter," shouted 3 from inside the Brain Gain Machine.

4 had to use lots of Brain Gain to make the pencil shorter, but at last it worked!

Which two pencils are the same length?

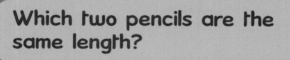

4 was ready to go back to base when Agent 16 called again! What now? The Problem Blob was splatting slime and a man's mop was getting **longer and longer**.

Here's the problem!

Who's this?

Splat! The mop was growing longer and longer!

The mop grew so long that it stretched into the café. It flipped food off the tables and caused a lot of trouble for everyone — especially for the waitress!

How do you think the cake got there?

5 thought about what might happen if other things carried on growing. Someone's nose might get longer. Or the dancing cow might get longer . . .

"We've got to stop that Problem Blob!" decided 5.

"Sending you more Brain Gain," said 6.

"I'm going to need lots," replied 4.

The man's mop squeaked and groaned as it got **shorter and shorter** – until it was too short!

"Oh no, that's too much shortening!" said 4.

"Now you'll have to think **longer** . . ." said the Agents.

After using a lot of Brain Gain, 4 finally managed to get the mop back to its normal size . . . and shrink the Problem Blob, too.

"Hooray!" everyone shouted.

"Bringing you back, number 4," said 5.

"I don't mind if you do," sighed 4.

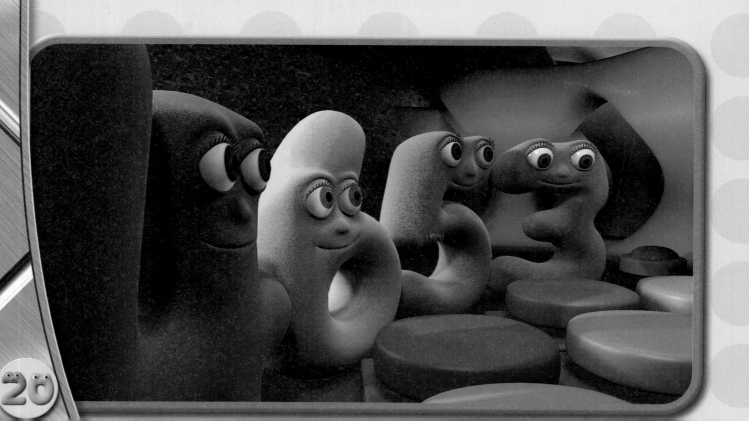

Everything looked back to normal again. But 4 was still worried.

"Are you sure everything's OK now?" 4 asked.

"See, the pencil is just the same length as all the others now," said 6.

"And, look. You've got a twin brother with a twin mop," said 5. "See, same lengths."

Check that the green pencil is the same length as the other ones.

"That's worth singing about," said 3. "La, la, la, la!"

"Oh no," groaned 4.

Thinky Bubble

Find two things that are the same length.

The Problem Blob has blobbed these things with green slime to make them shorter. Help sort out the problem.

Draw a **longer** stem and the leaves on this flower.

Draw a longer thread for this spider to dangle on.

Draw a longer string on this balloon.

Measuring

You can use many different things for measuring.

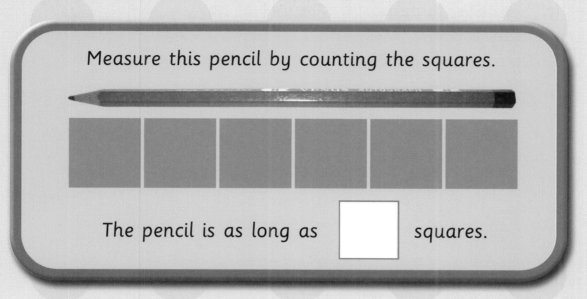

Measure this pencil by counting the squares.

The pencil is as long as [ ] squares.

Find something that is **taller** than this book.

Whose buddy blocks will make the tallest tower?
All of 3's pink buddy blocks or all of 4's blue buddy blocks?

Answers: the pencil is 6 squares long, 4's buddy blocks make the tallest tower.

23

Belongings

5, 4 and 3 were playing on the Thinkyjump Machine. "You have to think and jump on things that go together," said 5, jumping on pictures of an apple, then a banana. "They go together because they are fruit." Next, it was 3's turn.

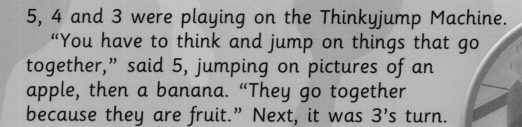

Do you think a dog and a cow go together?

"Yes! A dog and a cow go together because they are both animals," said 3.

Suddenly, they saw the alarm flashing. It was action stations for the Numberjacks! They raced to the Control Room.

5 zoomed up in the super-fast lift.

Agent 16 was on the Diamond Screen. "There's a boy wearing very strange clothes," said the Agent. "And look at this girl . . ."

Do these clothes belong to the children?

The girl was wearing a man's suit and the boy was wearing a lady's dress and straw hat! Something was going wrong!

Who was going to go out on the mission to put things right?

"5 knows about fashion," said 3.

"OK, I'll go," agreed 5.

"The Numberjacks are on their way," said 6.

5 jumped into the Launcher and waited for the all clear.

"Ready, go," said 6.

"Five, four, three, two, one, zero!" the Numberjacks counted down.

5 had just landed near the park when another Agent rang in with more problems!

"There's a man who isn't where he belongs — he's in a little kids' nursery!" the Agent told them.

"This is all very strange . . ." said 6. "Who's doing it?"

Who was going out on the mission?

Who doesn't belong in the nursery?

"Look!" said 5.
It was Spooky Spoon!
She floated down when she saw 5 on the path.

"Ugh! It's that horrible Numberjack 5," screeched Spooky Spoon. "Wonder what you're doing here?"

"I'm here to stop you mixing things up so they don't belong," replied 5.

"Oh, really. Well, in that case, you are going to be very disappointed . . . because you can't stop me!" she shrieked.

Spooky Spoon laughed loudly and floated off to see what else she could mix up.

Then a man ran through the park in swimming shorts and a boy went to his swimming lesson in a suit!

Who should be wearing which clothes?

"If Spooky Spoon goes on mixing things up anything could happen," said 5. "She might start mixing things up so creatures are in places where they don't belong . . ."

What would happen if an elephant was where a dog ought to be?

What was Spooky Spoon going to mix up next?
Suddenly, something went wrong with a man's meal in the café.

What has gone wrong with this man's meal?

He had a trainer to eat instead of a pizza!
"Mix! Mix! Mix!" laughed Spooky Spoon.
"What can we do?" said 6.
"Don't eat at that café for a start," joked 4.
"This is serious, 4," replied 3.

Agent 16 told them what to do. "Stop the mixing, start the matching," she said.

The Brain Gain Machine began to bubble and 3 jumped up and down inside it. "Think matching! Get things back together where they belong!" shouted 3.

Who is inside the Brain Gain Machine?

"We've got to match all the food things together," said 5.

Look at the pictures. Which things go together?

"You always spoil things for me," screeched Spooky Spoon. "You think you're so clever, 5."

"With help from my friends, yes, I'm clever enough to beat you," replied 5.

The Agents told 5 to trap Spooky Spoon in a circle with other things for eating with.

What other things do you use to eat with?

5 matched Spooky Spoon with a knife and a fork.

"Oh, no!" cried Spooky Spoon. She was stuck in a super-strong circle and couldn't get out.

"Now I can sort out all the things you've mixed up," said 5.

Soon everything was sorted out and back to where it belonged.

"Well done, 5," said 4.

"You sorted Spooky Spoon out," said 6.

"She thinks she's better than everyone else but she's just another thing to eat with!" said 3.

Thinky Bubble

Think of other things that belong together. What things go with a trainer?

29

Does it Belong?

5 has a problem! Spooky Spoon has been mixing things up again. Look at the picture to help 5 see what the problem is. Draw a circle around the thing that doesn't belong in the sky.

Draw **more** things that belong in the sky. Choose from these things, then think of **one more** thing yourself!

plane

car

sun

crab

Answers: the cow; the plane and the sun belong in the sky.

Stop Spooky Spoon!

Help the Numberjacks stop Spooky Spoon! You can trap her in this circle by drawing **two** things for eating with. Look, 4 is giving you a clue!

Now look at the Thinkyjump Machine. Which **two** things belong together? Draw **one more** thing that belongs with them.

Answers: knife and fork or spoon; cake and banana.

31

Trouble with Nothing!

You can help read this story. When you see the pictures of the Numberjacks, say their names.

Zero   **One**   **Three**   **Five**   **Six**

Numberjack was sorting out a problem.

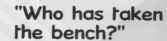

"Who has taken the bench?"

All sorts of things were disappearing.

A girl's ice cream, a boy's football and

a park bench had all

gone missing!

"Where's my ball?"

The Numberjacks looked closely and saw that 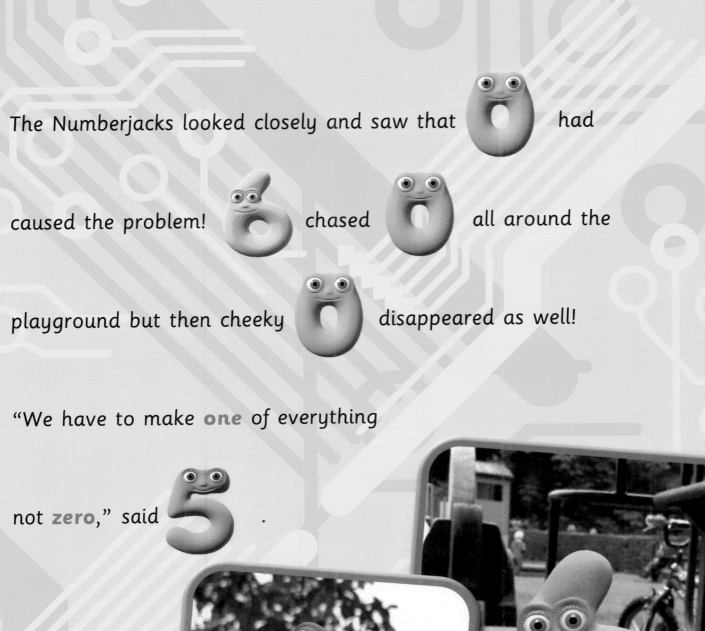 had caused the problem! 0 chased 0 all around the playground but then cheeky 0 disappeared as well!

"We have to make **one** of everything not **zero**," said 5.

When O showed up, things disappeared.

So went in the Brain Gain Machine.

"Think one!" said . Little did some great jumping

and the Brain Gain started to work!

The girl got her ice cream back and the boy got his football back.

The bench came back, too, but went missing again when

 appeared!

"Here's my ice cream!"

"Think one!"

"One!" said , and the bench reappeared.

"Zero!" said , and the bench disappeared!

Soon, was tired of jumping. Luckily for the Numberjacks,

 was feeling tired, too. At last, everything

was back to normal. "Hooray!" said the Numberjacks.

"Did the trick!" said .

"Time for your nap, O!"

Peace at last!

One Won

6 and 3 were in the Cosy Room. 6 was quietly reading a book but 3 was jumping about, being very noisy.

What was 6 doing?

Then little Numberjack 1 slid down the slide into the room.
"Hey, 1, we're making noises and jumping," said 3.
"Not all of us are," said 6, smiling.
1 made a little noise, **"Plooob"**, and did a little jump at the same time.

"La, la, la, la!"

"Plooob!"

"I can do just **one jump**," said 3.
"I bet you couldn't make just **one noise** though," said 6, joking.
Suddenly, the alarm rang loudly. The Numberjacks hurried to the Control Room as quickly as they could.

Agent 55 was on the Diamond Screen. "Things are going wrong! This girl used to have lots of toys," she said. "But now she hardly has any."

How many of each toy has the girl got?

"You're right. She hasn't got a lot of toys now," said 5.

What could the Numberjacks do?

"We'd better send someone out straight away!" said 5.

"I've had a good rest, I'm ready for a bit of action," said 6.

Who went in the launch pod?

Help the Numberjacks to count down to 6's launch.

6 5 4 3 2 1 0

6 landed safely and wasted no time in finding the little girl.

"Something has taken all the other toys and left only one of each," said Agent 70.

It was very odd.

Another Agent rang in to say that there was trouble at the garden centre.

"I think I can see the problem," said 6.

It was the Numbertaker!

"We need to watch out for things that there are more than one of," explained 5.

"What is he going to take next?" said 6.

Is there more than one thing here?

Is there more than one prong on the rake?

Is there more than one pot here?

Is there more than one hole on the watering can?

How could the Numberjacks stop the Numbertaker from taking things?

"He mustn't get to see anything if there's more than one of them," said Agent 55.

"OK," said 5. "We've got to spot things before the Numbertaker does and get them out of his sight."

5 thought about what might happen if he wasn't stopped . . .

What would happen to your cereal?

Only one leaf would be left on the flower.

This little girl wouldn't have anyone to play with because there is only one of her. Draw a friend for her.

"He's coming!" said 4.

"Oh, no! He'll be after you, 6!" said 3.

6 had an idea. "He won't grab 1. You've got to get number 1 out here!" said 6.

The Numberjacks made an emergency launch.

It was a very short countdown . . . "One, zero!" they counted.

"What can poor little 1 do against the great big Numbertaker?" asked 3, worried.

"Wait a minute, 1 doesn't have to be **little**, she can be **big** 1," said 5.

So the Numberjacks used Brain Gain to make 1 bigger.

"Think big, big, big, big!" shouted 3, jumping around inside the Brain Gain Machine.

The Agents joined in, too. "Think **scary big**," they said.

With the help of some very strong Brain Gain, little 1 became big 1, and looked so big and scary that the Numbertaker ran away!

Which numbers didn't 1 land on?

Why does 6 look so tiny?

big

bigger

All the Numberjacks up to 6 are here - except which number?

"Hooray!" they all shouted.

"Number 1 did the trick!" said 6. "Once 1 arrived and got bigger, that was the end of the Numbertaker."

Later, 3 and 6 were in the Cosy Room . . .
"You know you wanted me just to make one noise," said 3.
"Yes?" replied 6.
"Well, I can make just **one noise** – but it's going to be a **big one** . . ."

"YAY!"

Thinky Bubble

Have a look in your bedroom. What things have you got just one of?

41

Oh, no . . .

The Numbertaker is taking things – but only when there is **more than one** thing to take. Tick the box if the Numbertaker will take the things that are on the plate.

If the Numbertaker is looking for numbers more than one, do you think 4 is going to be safe?

... it's the Numbertaker!

The Numbertaker has been here already. He's left only **one** of each thing.

This butterfly can't fly with only one wing!

This fork hasn't got enough prongs!

This dice hasn't got enough dots!

Help the Numberjacks by drawing in the missing things.

Will 2 be safe from the Numbertaker if he takes numbers more than one?

Getting Heavy

3 and 4 were in the Gym playing on the seesaw with their buddy blocks.

Who has more buddy blocks: 3 or 4?

4 and the blue buddy blocks jumped on one end of the seesaw and 3 went flying through the air, almost landing on top of 9!

How many buddy blocks does 9 have?

"Sorry," said 3.

Just then, the alarm rang noisily. The Numberjacks rushed to the Control Room to see the Agent's call coming in.

"There's a boy having trouble with his backpack," said Agent 53.

"Hold on, I'm putting it on screen," said 4.

They saw a boy put an apple in his backpack, but when he put his backpack on, it pulled him down to the ground!

What could be wrong with the backpack?

"I can go!" said 3. "I've been practising jumping and everything."

"Well, OK, but I'm coming too," said 5.

Who went out on the mission to look after 3?

3 was very excited about going in the Launcher and not a bit nervous.

3 and 5 were soon ready for the launch but someone was on the sofa! 4 had to move them by ringing the doorbell.

What do you think the doorbell sounds like?

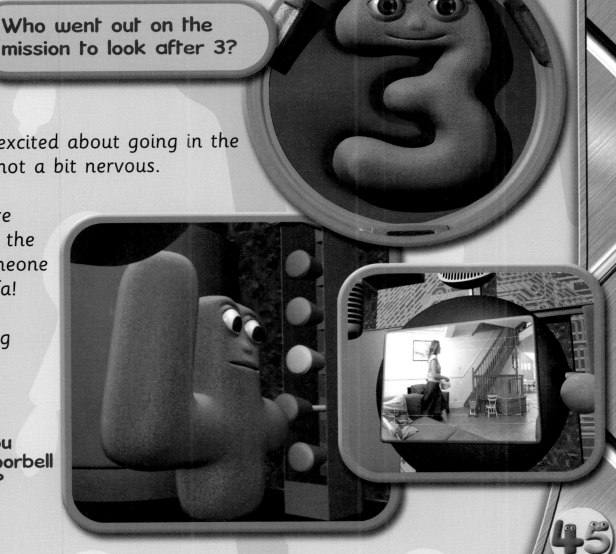

45

4 found a number 53 to land on, and straight away 5 and 3 went to check out the problem.

3 looked inside the bag and was surprised to see a **heavy** bowling ball!

Then Agent 85 rang in, "Quick, we've got more problems at the bowling alley!" she said.

The Numberjacks watched as a man threw a bowling ball and it turned into an apple! On his next throw, the bowling ball turned into a table tennis ball!

"Heavy things are being swapped for **light** things," explained Agent 16. **But who could be causing the problem?**

Which of these things is the lightest? Which is the heaviest?

"I am, of course!" shrieked Spooky Spoon, and she swooped down on 5 and 3.

"But why are you doing this?" 5 asked her.

"Because I want to, and if everyone's going down on the ground, I'm going to be on top," she boasted.

The next moment, a waitress in the café found a heavy bucket on her tray instead of a can of drink! Then, when a man was changing the wheel on his car, it turned into a pizza!

What could be inside the bucket to make it heavy?

Finally, tired out from all her stirring and swapping, Spooky Spoon rested, floating above the seesaw in the park.

Where do you think the wheel could have gone?

This little girl would like her balloon back. Find it on this page.

How could the Numberjacks get things back to normal?

"If you jump on one end of the seesaw you'll send Spooky Spoon into the air," said Agent 68.

But 5 and 3 weren't heavy enough to do that!

Which Numberjacks are in the Control Room?

"That bowling ball man is," said 3, looking at the man collecting the heavy bowling balls.

"Let's get him to think about having fun," said 6, turning the Brain Gain Machine on. **"Have fun! Jump! Jump! Have fun! Jump! Jump!"** 6 and the Agents chanted.

The powerful Brain Gain was sent to 5, who fired it at the man.

The man started to laugh out loud and dance around — and that woke up Spooky Spoon!

"What's going on?" she said, lifting up her head and yawning.

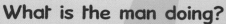

What is the man doing?

Then the man jumped on the end of the seesaw, sending Spooky Spoon soaring high into the air.

"Woahhh!" she cried out.

Who was heavier: Spooky Spoon or the man?

"She wanted to be higher than everyone else. And now she is!" joked 5.

Everyone cheered. It had been another great day for the Numberjacks!

Now the Numberjacks are back in the Gym, and they have a question for **you** . . .

Which side of the seesaw is higher?

Thinky Bubble

Which is heavier: a balloon or a banana?

Balancing Buddy Blocks

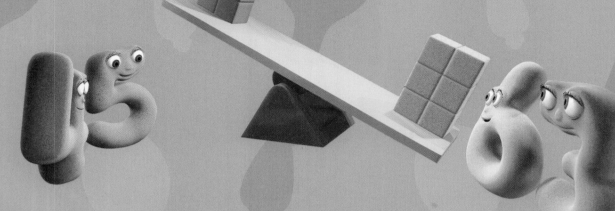

The seesaws will balance when each end has the same number of buddy blocks.
Draw the missing buddy blocks below to make each side the **same**.
Count and check each side.

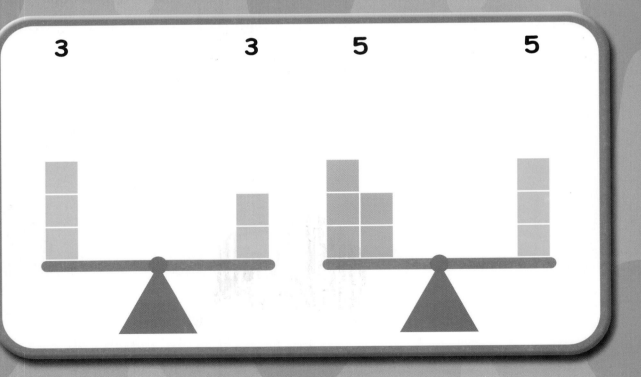

| 3 | 3 | 5 | 5 |

Close this book and place it on the palm of your hand.
Can you find something heavier and something lighter?

Answers: 3 each side; 5 each side.

Heavier or Lighter?

Spooky Spoon wants to mix up heavy and light things.
You can help to stop her with your clever thinking.

What is heavier than a dog?   What is lighter than a bull?

Look at the seesaws. Draw what you think could be on the other end.

What is lighter than a bath tub?

Which end of each seesaw is heavier? Can you say why?

2, 3 and 6 were in the Cosy Room looking at one of 3's Beautiful Things. "It's my best one," said 3.

1

"And look, it can turn into two Beautiful Things . . . and then fit back together again."

2

How many pieces was the Beautiful Thing split into?

Suddenly the alarm rang! The Numberjacks saw a girl and her drawing on the screen in the Control Room.

3

What was wrong with the girl's drawing?

"Half of her drawing has gone missing! And look at that lunch box!" said 5.

4

What was wrong with the lunch box?

5

Who was going out on the mission?

6

What was wrong with all these things?

There was only **half** a thing instead of a **whole** thing.
Who could be doing it?
4 spotted the Shape Japer! Can you see her too?

7

5 started thinking. "If the Shape Japer keeps on taking halves, people will be left with only half a book, or half a bed . . ." said 5.

How were the Numberjacks going to get all these half things back to whole things?

8

We've still got one half of these things. We need two halves to make them whole again.

6 had an idea. "Number 2 can make **two halves**!" So they put 2 in the Brain Gain Machine. "Two halves make a whole," said 6.

9

Two, two!

Have a good jump around.

With the help of Brain Gain, all of the half things soon became whole again!

10

What do two halves make?

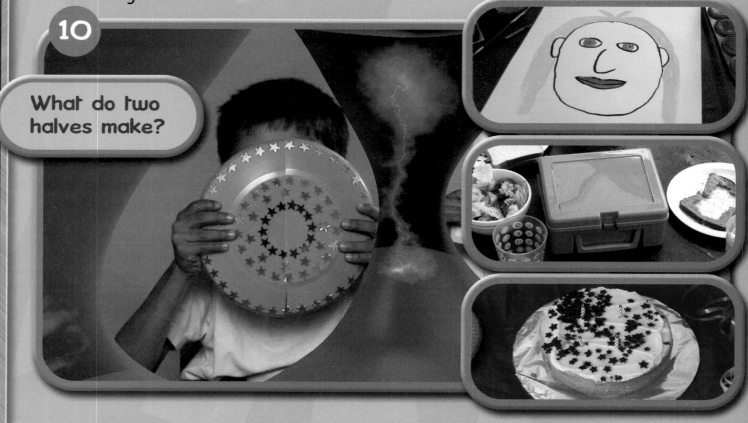

"We did it!" cheered the Numberjacks.
But how could the Numberjacks stop the Shape Japer from taking halves again?

11

4 thought of an answer. "Split her into two halves!" said 4. "One whole makes two halves," said the Agents.

12

13

4 used some more Brain Gain to split the Shape Japer into two halves! And it worked! She wasn't very happy. But everyone else was!

14

Do you have anything that you can split in half to share with a friend?

"Hooray!" said all the Numberjacks. "Nice work, 2 and 4!" said 6.

Shoo, Shape Japer!

The Shape Japer's back and she's stealing halves again!

Can you help 4 to sort out the problem?
Draw the **missing half** of each of these
things and then say, "Shoo, Shape Japer, shoo!"

You can try making halves yourself.

"Making halves is like sharing!" says 3.
Draw a line down the middle of each of these
things to make two parts. The first one is done for you.
Try to make the parts the same size so that they are **equal halves**.

Nine Lives

You can help read this story. When you see the pictures of the Numberjacks or the Puzzler, say their names.

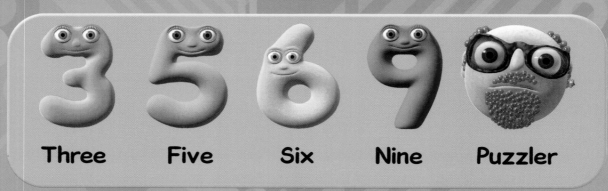

Three **Five** **Six** **Nine** **Puzzler**

 and  were on a mission to find out why a boy's

3 wheels had suddenly turned into **6** wheels and then **9** wheels!

It was very strange.

Which numbers did 6 and 3 land on?

36

How many wheels in each group? How many wheels altogether?

Which Numberjack is in front and which one is behind?

But that wasn't all. They saw a lady carrying **3** parcels which

suddenly changed into **6** parcels

How many parcels can you see in the picture?

and then **9** parcels!

What could be happening?

 began to think about

the problem. Imagine if it were

Goldilocks and the **9** bears . . .

"Who could be doing this?"  asked. "Look!" said  .

It was the  . Yes, he was the problem!

"Your friend is inside my bubble!" he told them.

"I'll let  go free when I see 3, 3 and 3!"

Now the Numberjacks had to

rescue as well.

Which Numberjack was inside the bubble?

What is wrong with the Puzzler's face?

The Agents rang in to help solve the puzzle. "Numberjack is one 3," said the Agents. "And you could change into the

other two 3s."  sent some powerful Brain Gain to

help . It worked! became **two yellow 3s!**

Get 6 things and check that you can make 6 into two lots of 3!

Who was in the Brain Gain Machine?

How many 3s can you see?

Now that they had  , and , they thought the

 would set free – but he didn't! He gave them

another puzzle! He told them to make **1 square** from **9 squares**.

They were looking for some squares when  spotted **9**

square napkins.

Which is the real
Numberjack 3?
How can you tell?

How many sides
does a square have?

They put the napkins together in **3** rows of **3** – and do you

know what they made? They made **1** square from **9** small squares.

They'd solved the puzzle! Now the  had to

set  free! The Numberjacks were so glad when everything

went back to normal – including  !

How many napkins are there altogether?

Which Numberjack has turned into two 3s?

Is 6 back to normal now?

Which of these pictures shows the Shape Japer as a **square**?

a   **b**   **c**

Whose buddy blocks have made these prints?

Can you see any squares in this house picture.
Look for little squares inside bigger ones, too.

Answers: c; from left to right – Numberjacks 1, 4 and 9; the windows are square.

Burst the Bubble!

The Puzzler has blown another big bubble and has trapped 6 inside!

Can you show 6 the way out and burst the Puzzler's bubble?

start

POP!!

Slides and Lifts

You will need a counter for each player, a dice and a friend to play this game with.

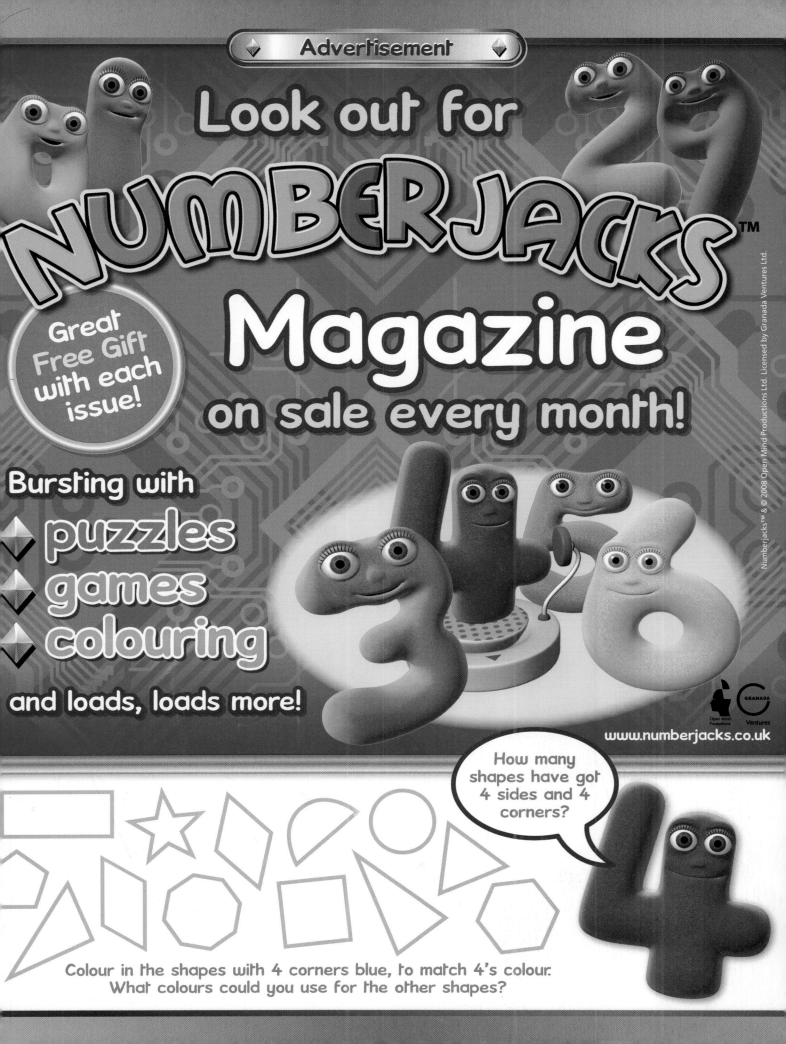